Contents

Why buy this book?

The 100 Lessons series has been designed to support the introduction of the new National Curriculum in schools in England. The new curriculum is more challenging in English and includes the requirement for children's understanding to be secure before moving on. These practice books will help your child practise all of the skills they will learn at school, including some topics they might not have encountered previously.

How to use this book

- The content is divided into National Curriculum topics (for example, Spelling, Grammar, Comprehension and so on). Find out what your child is doing in school and dip into the relative practice activities as required.

- Let your child know you are sharing the activities and support if necessary using the helpful quick tips at the top of most pages.

- Keep the working time short and come back to an activity if your child finds it too difficult. Ask your child to note any areas of difficulty. Don't worry if your child does not 'get' a concept first time, as children learn at different rates and content is likely to be covered throughout the school year.

- Check your child's answers using the answers section on www.scholastic.co.uk/100practice/englishy4

- You will also find additional interactive activities for your child to play on the website.

- Give lots of encouragement and tick off the progress chart as your child completes each chapter.

How to use the book

This tells you which topic you're working on.

This is the title of the activity.

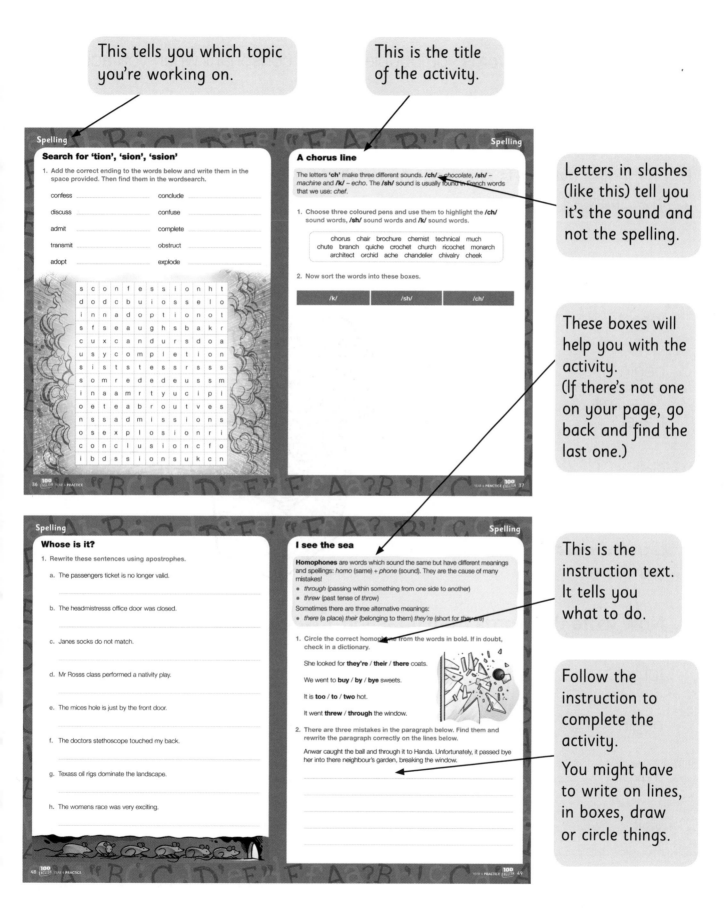

Letters in slashes (like this) tell you it's the sound and not the spelling.

These boxes will help you with the activity. (If there's not one on your page, go back and find the last one.)

This is the instruction text. It tells you what to do.

Follow the instruction to complete the activity.

You might have to write on lines, in boxes, draw or circle things.

If you need help, ask an adult!

Adding 'ing'

Remember, for some words you double the last consonant when you add a suffix:

- *hop – ho**pp**ing*
- *control – contro**ll**ing*

But if the first syllable is stressed you don't:

- *visit – visi**t**ing*

1. **Underline the syllable which is stressed in these two-syllable words.**

forget

begin

travel

visit

permit

admit

2. **Now write the words from question 1 with an 'ing' ending.**

forget _____   limit _____

begin _____   target _____

travel _____   regret _____

visit _____   prefer _____

permit _____   fuel _____

admit _____   focus _____

Doubling up

The two suffixes **'ing'** and **'ed'** are often used at the end of verbs.

They tell us what's happen**ing** today and what has already happen**ed**.

Sometimes when you add **'ing'** or **'ed'** to a word the last consonant doubles up.

1. **Look carefully at the words in the balloon baskets. Add 'ing' or 'ed'**
   to the words and write them in the balloons.

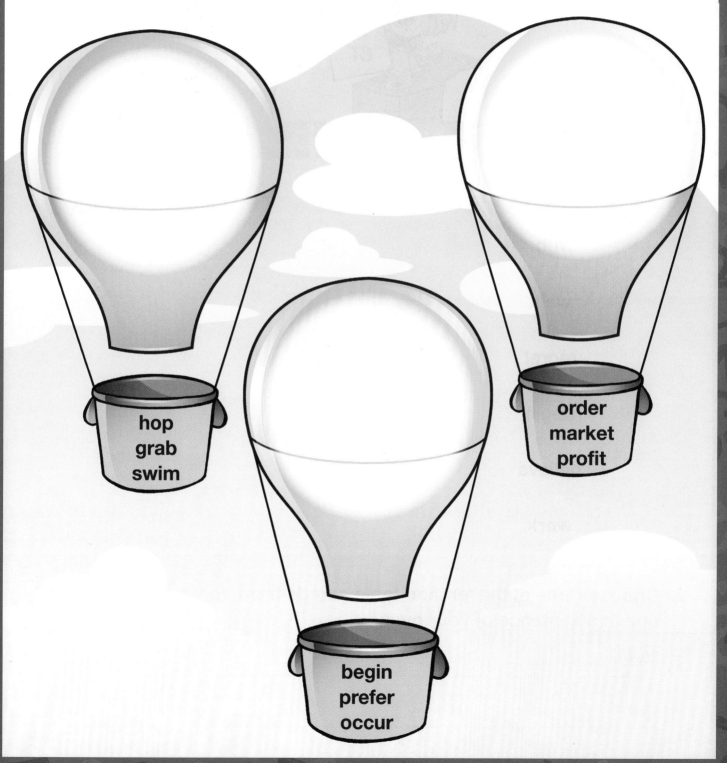

hop
grab
swim

begin
prefer
occur

order
market
profit

Adding 'er', 'able'

You can add the suffix **'er'** or **'able'** to some words to make new words.

Words ending in **'e'**, drop the **'e'** before adding **'er'** or **'able'**:

- *value – valuable*

1. **Add 'er' or 'able' to these words.**

	er	able
forget		
rub		
walk		
regret		
begin		
believe		
work		

2. **Choose three of the 'er' and 'able' words from question 1. Use each one in a sentence of your own.**

_____

_____

Words ending in 'l'

Remember – in words like *hop* and *control*, you double the final consonant before adding a suffix. Look at page 6 for a reminder.

1. **All of these words end in 'l'. Put them through the suffix machine and write new correct words.**

peel

marvel

peril

control

novel

final

travel

propel

signal

jewel

football

'i' or 'y'?

In some words the long vowel **/igh/** sound is spelled with a **'y'**: *spy, by, my*.
BUT in some words the short vowel **/i/** sound can also be spelled with a **'y'**, such as *gym*.

1. The words below are not spelled correctly. Correct them by changing the **'i'** to a **'y'**.

histerical

simptom

lirics

simmetry

simpathy

cristal

sistem

mistery

tipical

cignet

/i/ wordsearch

1. Find the words for the wordsearch from the meanings below.

A shape with four triangle sides
and one square bottom:

_____

A story that isn't true:

_____

A dinosaur that flies:

_____

Something that we breathe:

_____

The words of a song written
down:

_____

A young swan:

_____

A clear transparent rock:

_____

Something strange or not known:

_____

m	y	s	t	e	r	y	h
u	c	o	h	y	o	r	d
p	y	r	a	m	i	d	u
t	g	a	l	y	l	a	k
e	n	u	y	t	o	w	l
r	e	o	f	h	c	r	m
o	t	x	o	y	r	e	n
d	u	y	i	r	y	y	o
a	i	g	n	e	s	n	p
c	g	e	d	w	t	h	y
t	h	n	f	b	a	x	s
y	r	e	x	n	l	o	i
l	y	r	i	c	s	i	n

Encourage the 'ou'

Sometimes the letters **'ou'** make the sound **/u/**.

1. **Complete each sentence by adding an 'ou' word from the box.**

> touch   young   country   double   cousin
> couple   flourish   tough   encourage

a. Don't _____ the statue or it will fall over.

b. The _____ man ran the marathon.

c. I went to live in another _____.

d. There is a _____ of apples in the bowl.

e. The teacher said he would _____

   our homework because we were not listening.

f. My _____ lives in New York.

g. Your cactus will occasionally need water if you want

   it to _____.

h. It was a _____ climb but we made it!

i. I think I will _____ my friend to

   enter the auditions.

What's the meaning?

1. **Draw lines to match the 'ou' word with its meaning.**

country   Having lived for a short time.

encourage   To grow successfully.

hound   A light dessert made from egg and sugar.

mousse   Baked to make bread.

nourish   To try to make someone or something do something.

flourish   Two things together.

dough   Another word for a dog.

couple   To give food for things to grow healthily.

young   A place where people live.

2. **Find three 'ou' words above which do not sound /u/ and write them below. Can you think of other words where 'ou' sounds the same?**

_____   _____

_____   _____

_____   _____

3. **Choose two of the words in question 1. Use them in a sentence of your own.**

_____

_____

'dis' or 'mis'?

When you add the prefixes **'dis'** and **'mis'** to words, you change their meaning.

- **'dis'** means *not* or *opposite of.*
- **'mis'** means *not* or *wrong.*

1. **Change the meaning of these words by putting them through the 'dis' or 'mis' prefix hats.**

advantage

match

pleasure

behave

order

place

connect

fortune

direct

appear

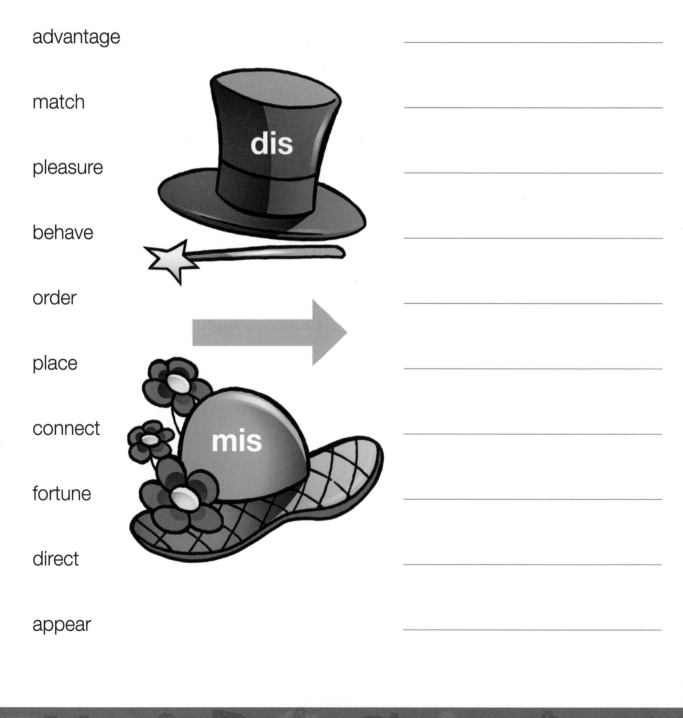

Irregular and illogical

When you add the prefixes **'ir'** and **'il'** to words, you change their meaning.
- **'il'** and **'ir'** mean *not*.

1. Find the meaning of these words using a dictionary.

> legal   logical   regular   resistible   reversible   rational

2. Add **'il'** or **'ir'** to each word from question 1 to create correct new words. Use each one in a sentence of your own.

a. _____

_____

b. _____

_____

c. _____

_____

d. _____

_____

e. _____

_____

f. _____

_____

'in' or 'im'?

Here are two more prefixes which change a word from one meaning into its opposite.

● **'in'** and **'im'** mean *not*.

1. Add 'im' or 'in' to these words to make their opposites.

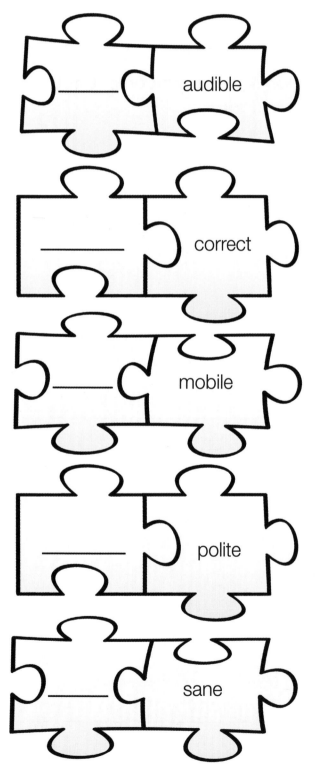

_____ audible

_____ correct

_____ mobile

_____ polite

_____ sane

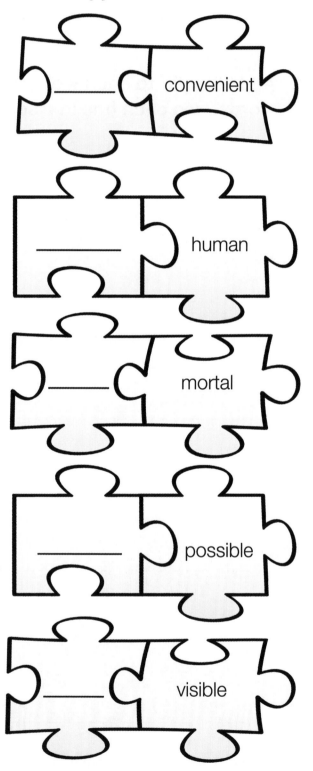

_____ convenient

_____ human

_____ mortal

_____ possible

_____ visible

Prefix crossword

1. The words in the box below begin with the prefixes **'dis'**, **'mis'**, **'in'**, **'ir'**, **'il'**, **'im'**. Match them to the clues to find the answers to the crossword.

> disappeared   illogical   misplaced   invisible
> irresistible   impossible   irregular

Across	Down
2. That cake looks too delicious.	1. That is a strange way of doing that!
4. Something that cannot be done.	3. It cannot be seen.
5. That doesn't make sense!	6. It was there a minute ago, but now it is not!
7. It has been put somewhere else.	

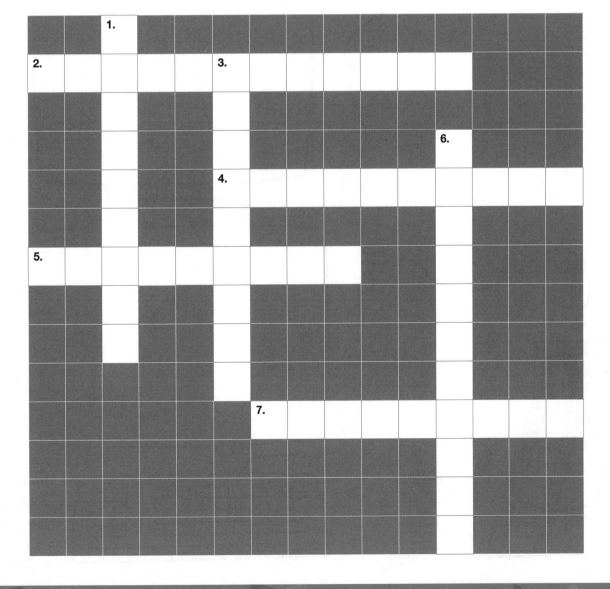

Muddled words

- The prefix **'re'** means *again* or *back*.
- The prefix **'inter'** means *between* or *among*.

1. Add the correct prefix and write the words in the boxes.

lude   fresh   related   appear   decorate
treat   continental   arrange   face   mingle

re

inter

Add the correct word

1. Add the correct 're' or 'inter' word to complete these sentences.

recover   redecorate   rearrange   retreat   international
interface   interval   intergalactic

a. I need to _____ after running the race.

b. The _____ on the computer looks odd.

c. The _____ is usually in the middle of the

performance.

d. The librarian will need to _____ the books.

e. The _____ space cruiser docked safely at

Saturn Beta.

f. The painter must _____ the room.

g. Global Baggage is an _____ chain of hotels.

h. When I don't want to do my homework, I _____

to my room.

Super sub prefix machine

- **'sub'** means *under* or *below*.
- **'super'** means *above*, *over* or *beyond*.

1. Add **'super'** or **'sub'** to these words to make new real words.

category _____

standard _____

computer _____

editor _____

sonic _____

impose _____

merge _____

power _____

2. Create some new words by adding **'sub'** or **'super'** to words you know.

_____ _____

_____ _____

_____ _____

3. **Use the words from question 1 and write them next to their meanings.**

Secondary group: _____

Speed greater than sound: _____

To cover with water: _____

Assistant text corrector: _____

A powerful machine: _____

Poor quality: _____

Put one image over another: _____

Abilities beyond anyone else: _____

'anti' and 'auto'

- **'anti'** means *against*.
- **'auto'** means *self*.

1. Use the prefix machine to add **'anti'** or **'auto'** to these words and write them in the space provided.

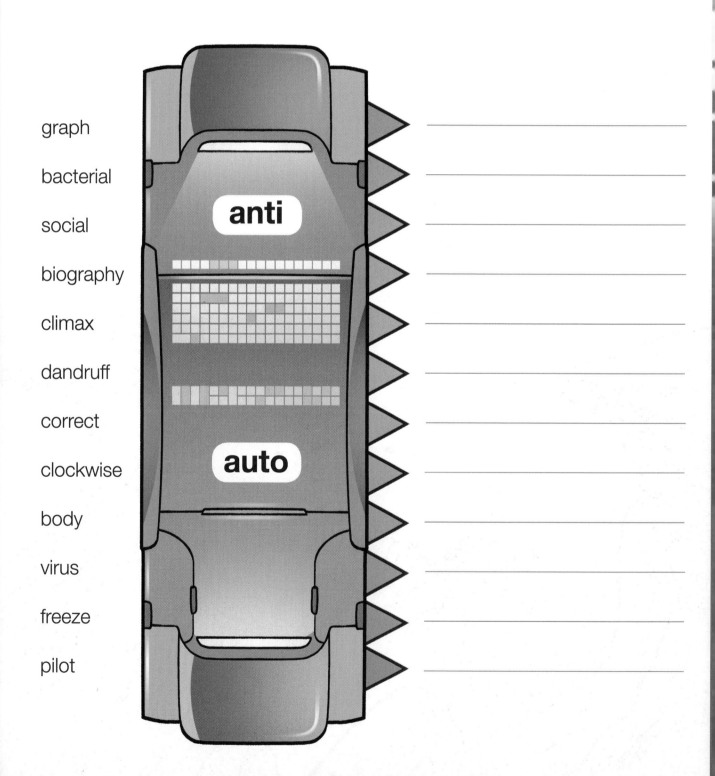

graph

bacterial

social

anti

biography

climax

dandruff

correct

auto

clockwise

body

virus

freeze

pilot

Match the meanings

1. **Read the meanings below then find the matching 'anti' or 'auto' word from page 22.**

   Something which amends itself: _____.

   Something which stops white flakes in your hair:

   _____.

   Something that kills germs: _____.

   A book written about yourself: _____.

2. **Draw a line to match each new made-up word to its meaning.**

   anti + sister = antisister   A virus that stops you going to school.

   anti + school = antischool   A robot mum.

   auto + mum = automum   An automatic room cleaner.

   auto + room= autoroom   A spray which stops your sister from
                                       annoying you.

3. **Make some new words by adding 'anti' or 'auto' to words you know.**

   _____

   _____

Adding 'ation'

Adding **'ation'** to a verb changes it into a noun.

- Most words just add **'ation'**: *inform – information*
- If the words ends in **'e'**, take off the **'e'** before adding **'ation'**: *sense – sensation*
- If the word ends in **'ate'**, take off the **'ate'** before adding **'ation'**: *accelerate – acceleration*
- If the words ends in **'y'**, change the **'y'** to **'ic'** before adding **'ation'**: *classify – classification*

1. **Add 'ation' to the words below following the rules above.**

admire _____

relocate _____

justify _____

translate _____

animate _____

educate _____

observe _____

accommodate _____

anticipate _____

identify _____

The missing 'ation'

1. Look at these words. Look them up in a dictionary if you need to.

> admiration   relocation   justification   translation   animation   education
> observation   accommodation   anticipation   identification

2. Use the words from question 1 to complete these sentences.

a. I was full of _____ when my friend won the cup.

b. I could not do the _____ from French to English.

c. The hotel did not have any _____ available.

d. The _____ costs were going to be huge,

so my dad didn't move.

e. The _____ was about a dog and was very funny.

f. The _____ of seeing my best friend after

the holidays was too much.

g. I want to get an _____ so I can get myself a job.

h. The _____ tag was

still on the dog so we found a phone number.

i. I didn't agree with the _____

for not letting us outside at playtime.

j. The teacher assessed the children by _____.

Quickly

An **adverb** describes a verb. Some adverbs are made by adding **'ly'** to adjectives. In the sentence *She ran quickly*, the adverb *quickly* tells us how she ran.

1. **Add a different adverb to each of the following sentences.**

   a. Mr James ran _____.

   b. He drove _____.

   c. It rained _____.

   d. The car stopped _____.

   e. She laughed _____.

   f. Jim answered _____.

   g. The music played _____.

   h. The girl sighed _____.

   i. Jake did his homework _____.

   j. Time passed _____.

2. **Underline the adverbs in *Escape*.**

Escape

He ran quickly down the street. He looked anxiously left and right. Fortunately everything was quiet. He felt tired and rather unhappy to be running away so soon. He reached the crossroads and stopped momentarily. He started again and turned cautiously into the High Street. Suddenly he stopped. There was the sound of footsteps behind him. His heart beat violently. He was being followed!

Adjective to adverb

If the adjective ends in **'y'**, change the **'y'** to **'i'**, then add the **'ly'**.
hungry – hungrily

1. **Change the adjectives in the first column into adverbs. The first one has been done for you.**

Adjective	Adverb
angry	angrily
anxious	
bad	
careful	
clumsy	
correct	
greedy	
happy	
hungry	
immediate	
quiet	
serious	

Adding 'ly' to words ending in 'le'

If the adjective ends in consonant + **'le'**, remove **'le'** and add **'ly'**.

If the adjective ends in vowel + **'le'**, just add **'ly'**.

For example: *simple – simply* but *sole – solely*.

1. **Change these adjectives into adverbs following the rule.**

Adjective	Adverb
incredible	_____
hostile	_____
probable	_____
agile	_____
terrible	_____

2. **Use the words you created in question 1 to complete these sentences.**

"Well, I think we're _____ looking at a world record, Jeff."

"Sure, Matt. The boy's _____ talented."

"He moves so _____ – on this apparatus, there's no knowing what he's capable of."

"And now he's fallen! The crowd are reacting quite _____ about that."

"What a _____ embarrassing moment for team GB."

Adding 'ly' to words ending in 'ic'

If the adjective ends in **'ic'**, add **'al'** before **'ly'**: *basic – basically.*

1. **Change these adjectives into adverbs by sending them round the prefix roundabouts.**

dramatic

frantic

historic

domestic

energetic

diplomatic

robotic

tragic

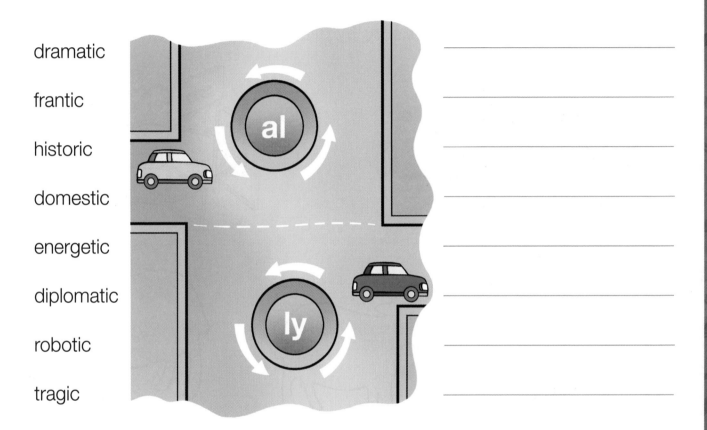

2. **Choose four adverbs from question 1. Use them in sentences of your own.**

Sheep enclosure

Words that end with the sound **/zh/er/** are always spelled with **'sure'**: *enclo**sure***.

But **'sure'** can make other sounds, for example the **/sh/er/** sound in *as**sure***.

1. **Add 'sure' to the end of the words below. Put the 'sure' word sheep back into the correct enclosure by drawing lines.**

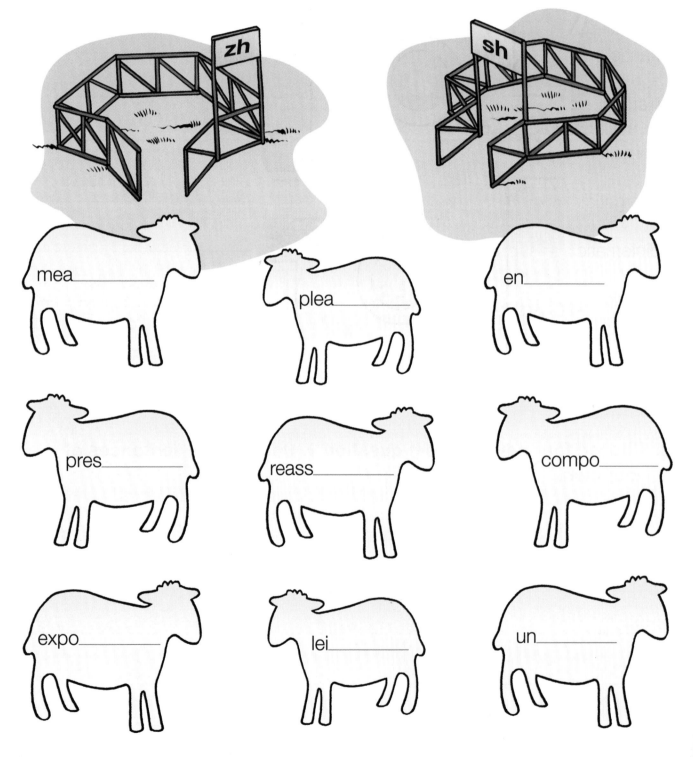

zh

sh

mea_____

plea_____

en_____

pres_____

reass_____

compo_____

expo_____

lei_____

un_____

What's in the picture?

Words that end in the sound **/ch/er/** can be spelled **'ture'**.

1. Find the ten **'ture'** words in the picture and write them down.

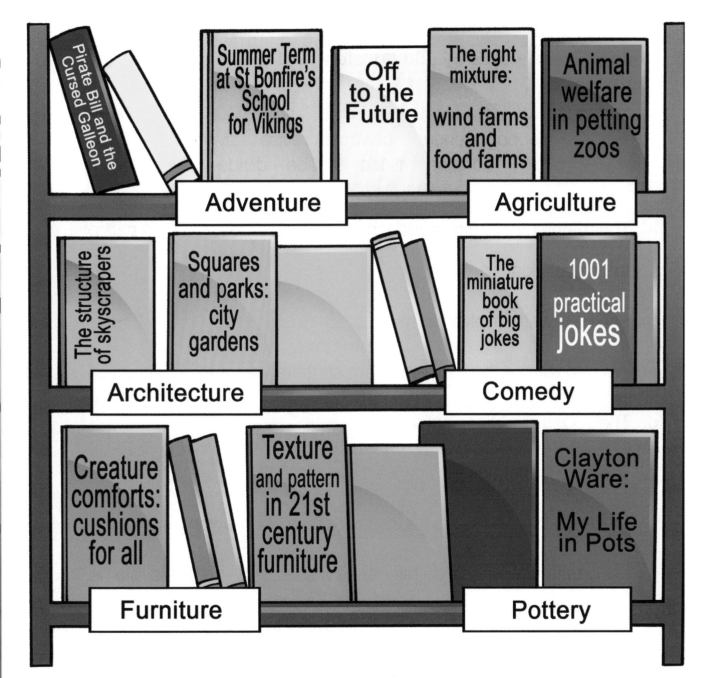

_____

_____

_____

A diversion

When a word ends with the sound **/zh/u/n/**, it is always spelled **'sion'**: *erosion*.

Remember to take off the **'d'**, **'de'** or **'se'** before adding **'sion'**: *erode – erosion*.

1. **Change these words by adding 'sion' and then complete the sentences.**

> comprehend   corrode   revise   divert
> confuse   allude   collide   divide

a. The maths problem required long _____ as part of

the calculation.

b. The cars were involved in a _____.

c. We had to take the left road because there was a _____.

d. The wrong directions caused _____.

e. The hole in the pipe was caused by _____.

f. I managed to do my _____ homework.

g. My brother is trying to do his _____ for his exams.

h. I made an _____ to going to the party.

How to add 'ous'

Adding **'ous'** to a verb or a noun makes an adjective.

- Most words just add **'ous'**: *poison – poisonous*
- Words ending in **'e'**, take off the **'e'** before adding **'ous'**: *fame – famous*
- Words ending in **'y'**, take off the **'y'** and add **'i'** before adding **'ous'**: *vary – various*
- Keep the **'e'** if the word ends with a **/j/** sound before adding **'ous'**: *outrage – outrageous*

1. **Use the rules above to add 'ous' to these words.**

courage _____

harmony _____

envy _____

poison _____

glory _____

fame _____

vary _____

adventure _____

luxury _____

outrage _____

What do you do?

1. Look at these pictures of people doing their jobs. Write the appropriate 'cian' word underneath.

politics	diet	beauty
music	optics	physics
electricity	magic	mathematics

'tion', 'sion', 'ssion', 'cian' assembly line

Words which end with the sound **/sh/u/n/** can be spelled in four different ways: **'tion'**, **'sion'**, **'ssion'** or **'cian'**.
Remember:

- To add **'tion'** take off the **'t'** or **'te'** first.
- To add **'sion'** take off the **'d'**, **'se'** or **'de'** first.
- To add **'ssion'** take off the **'ss'** or **'mit'** first.
- To add **'cian'** take off the **'s'** or **'cs'** first.

1. Add the correct ending – **'tion'**, **'sion'**, **'ssion'** or **'cian'** – to the words in the assembly line using the rules above. Remember that when words end in **'e'**, you take the **'e'** off before adding the prefix.

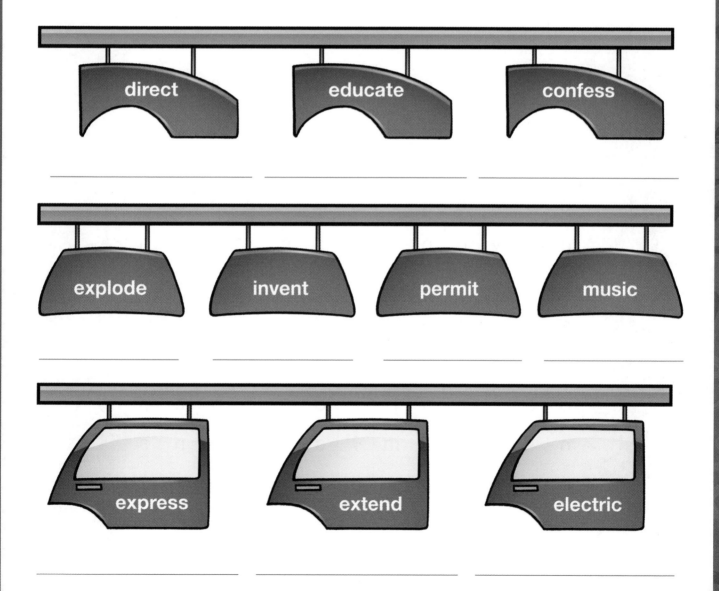

direct   educate   confess

explode   invent   permit   music

express   extend   electric

Search for 'tion', 'sion', 'ssion'

1. **Add the correct ending to the words below and write them in the space provided. Then find them in the wordsearch.**

confess _____   conclude _____

discuss _____   confuse _____

admit _____   complete _____

transmit _____   obstruct _____

adopt _____   explode _____

s	c	o	n	f	e	s	s	i	o	n	h	t
d	o	d	c	b	u	i	o	s	s	e	l	o
i	n	n	a	d	o	p	t	i	o	n	o	t
s	f	s	e	a	u	g	h	s	b	a	k	r
c	u	x	c	a	n	d	u	r	s	d	o	a
u	s	y	c	o	m	p	l	e	t	i	o	n
s	i	s	t	s	t	e	s	s	r	s	s	s
s	o	m	r	e	d	e	d	e	u	s	s	m
i	n	a	a	m	r	t	y	u	c	i	p	i
o	e	t	e	a	b	r	o	u	t	v	e	s
n	s	s	a	d	m	i	s	s	i	o	n	s
o	s	e	x	p	l	o	s	i	o	n	r	i
c	o	n	c	l	u	s	i	o	n	c	f	o
i	b	d	s	s	i	o	n	s	u	k	c	n

A chorus line

The letters **'ch'** make three different sounds. **/ch/** – *chocolate*, **/sh/** – *machine* and **/k/** – *echo*. The **/sh/** sound is usually found in French words that we use: *chef*.

1. Choose three coloured pens and use them to highlight the **/ch/** sound words, **/sh/** sound words and **/k/** sound words.

> chorus   chair   brochure   chemist   technical   much
> chute   branch   quiche   crochet   church   ricochet   monarch
> architect   orchid   ache   chandelier   chivalry   cheek

2. Now sort the words into these boxes.

/k/	/sh/	/ch/

The 'ch' machine

Remember, **'ch'** can be said in three different ways: **/ch/, /sh/, /k/**.

1. **Complete the sentences below by writing the correct 'ch' word.**

2. **Then write 'ch', 'sh' or 'k' to show how the word you have written is pronounced.**

> stomach   chalet   scheme   orchestra   parachute
> architect   moustache   chandelier

The _____ dangled from the ceiling. ☐

I have a _____ ache. ☐

There is a wooden _____ on the hill. ☐

I have a _____ to not do my homework. ☐

The man played the violin in the _____. ☐

The _____ drew pictures of the house. ☐

The man had a neat _____. ☐

I jumped from the aeroplane with a _____. ☐

'gue' and 'que'

Words that have the endings **'gue'** and **'que'** mostly originate from French words. In French, the letter **'q'** is pronounced **/k/**.

'gue' sound like **/g/**: *plague*   **'que'** sounds like **/k/**: *plaque*

1. **Complete the words below with either 'gue' or 'que'. Write the finished words into the correct buildings.**

HOTEL GUE

monolo_____

brus_____

travelo_____

statues_____

fati_____

mysti_____

prolo_____

pictures_____

HOTEL QUE

2. **Choose one 'gue' word and one 'que' word from question 1. Write them in sentences of your own.**

_____

_____

_____

Searching for 'que' and 'gue'

1. **Find the words below in the wordsearch.**

grotesque opaque fatigue

physique unique intrigue

antique colleague

p	h	y	s	i	q	u	e	q
i	q	u	e	s	c	i	f	u
n	u	n	i	q	u	e	a	e
t	g	r	u	f	n	b	t	g
r	u	d	a	s	u	g	i	u
i	e	c	n	s	e	u	g	e
g	r	o	t	e	s	q	u	e
u	c	i	i	a	s	c	e	t
e	n	o	q	g	u	e	l	i
q	u	e	u	f	q	u	e	l
g	h	b	e	a	d	d	t	h
o	p	a	q	u	e	b	h	d
c	o	l	l	e	a	g	u	e

The science of 'sc'

In some words the **/s/** is made by **'sc'**. These words come from older Latin words and in Roman times **'c'** was probably pronounced as **'s'**.

1. **Complete the sentences with the 'sc' words from the box.**

> ascend   crescent   descend   fascinated   scene
> scenery   scent   science   scientist   scissors

a. I began to _____ the hill to get to the top.

b. A _____ moon is not very bright.

c. The farmer had to _____ the hill with his sheep.

d. I was _____ with the picture in the gallery.

e. The _____ was very beautiful.

f. The _____ of the perfume was quite strong.

g. I had to use the _____ to cut the string.

h. The _____ discovered a cure for the common cold.

2. **You did not use two of the words in question 1. Use these words in sentences of your own.**

_____

_____

_____

_____

S(c)ounds like

1. **All of these words use 'sc' in their spelling but they don't all sound the same. Sort the words according to their sound.**

scented   descent   discipline   adolescent   escape
scream   scooter   oscillate   ascent   score   disco   scarf

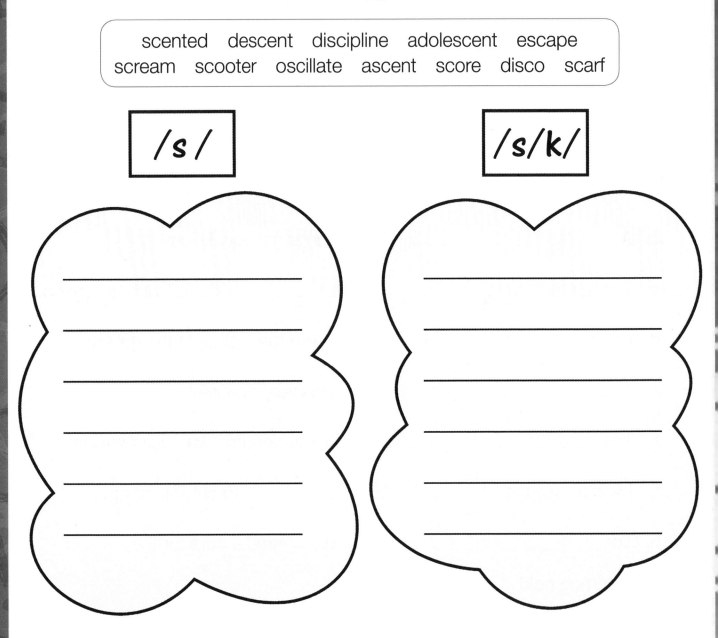

/s/

/s/k/

2. **Look at the two groups of words.**

What letters follow **'sc'** in words that sound like **/s/**?

_____

What letters follow **'sc'** in words that sound like **/sk/**?

_____

Correct the spelling

The sound **/ai/** can be spelled in lots of different ways: **'a–e'**, **'ai'**, **'ay'**, **'ei'**, **'eigh'** and **'ey'**! There is no rule, they just have to be learned.

1. **These words are not spelled correctly. Write the correct spellings using the meanings to help you.**

whay	_____	You separate this to make cheese.
nai	_____	The sound a horse makes.
slaigh	_____	Transport for snowy weather.
rayn	_____	Horses have these.
convai	_____	To tell or pass on information.
wai	_____	To measure how heavy something is.
prai	_____	You can go to a place of worship to do this.
preigh	_____	An animal that is being hunted.
vail	_____	A bride might wear one.

/ai/ sound

a astray away bay betray
castaway clay convey day
decay delay dismay disobey
display eight essay fray grey
holiday hooray jay lay may

mislay nay neigh neighbour
obey pay play portray pray
prey ray repay say sleigh
spray stay stray subway sway
they vein weigh yesterday

1. **Look at this extract from a rhyming dictionary with words that have the long /ai/ vowel sound. Find suitable words to complete the second and last verses of this ballad.**

Silly Billy

Now, here's the tale of Billy boy,

A tale we should all convey.

For Billy acted without thought,

He's a silly boy today.

Now Billy was a silly boy,

He just wanted to _____

So instead of going to school one day

He ran away in a _____

Now Billy was a silly boy,

He didn't want to _____

And now instead of being at school,

He's led himself _____

Apostrophes

Apostrophes can be used to show that something belongs to someone or something.

- *The dog's basket* – the basket belongs to the dog

1. **Read the sentences below. Circle the words that are missing the possessive apostrophe and write them correctly.**

   a. The strong wind blew Olivias umbrella away. _____

   b. The rain battered the horses stable. _____

   c. I saw the rabbits tail. _____

   d. The man fixed the boats rudder. _____

   e. The dogs ball rolled under the fence. _____

   f. I looked at my friends picture. _____

   g. The cars brakes squealed when it stopped. _____

   h. I like my brothers new bike. _____

Spot the apostrophe

Can you spot the difference?

The pirate's treasure.   **The pirates' treasure.**

1. Put in the apostrophes.

The monkeys tail   **The monkeys tails**

The girls pencils   **The girls pencils**

Look at these unusual ones.

The children's chocolate   The fairy's wands   The fairies' wands

2. Now put the apostrophes in these.

The babys nappies   The ladys shoe

The babies nappies   The ladies shoe

Irregular plurals and apostrophes

There are some plurals that are irregular and do not end in an **'s'**. To make the possessive, add apostrophe and **'s'** to these irregular words: *mice – mice's*

When a singular proper noun ends in **'s'** then you add an apostrophe and another **'s'**: Lewis – Lewis's

1. **Put these irregular nouns through the apostrophe tunnel.**

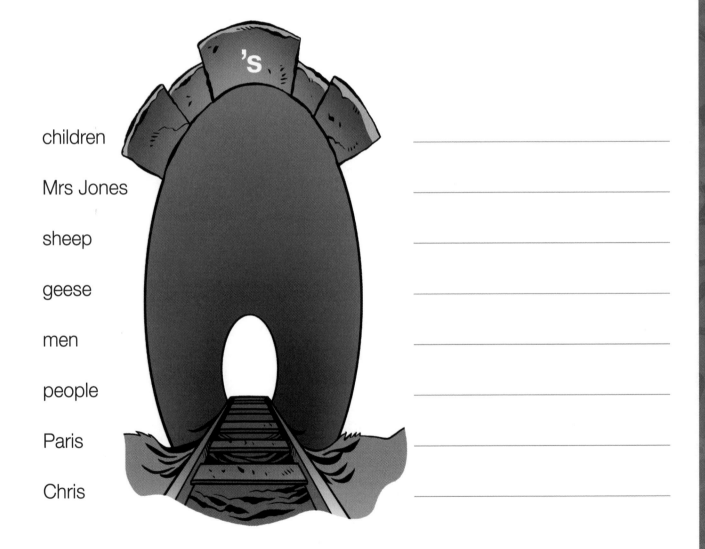

children _____

Mrs Jones _____

sheep _____

geese _____

men _____

people _____

Paris _____

Chris _____

Whose is it?

1. **Rewrite these sentences using apostrophes.**

   a. The passengers ticket is no longer valid.

   _____

   b. The headmistresss office door was closed.

   _____

   c. Janes socks do not match.

   _____

   d. Mr Rosss class performed a nativity play.

   _____

   e. The mices hole is just by the front door.

   _____

   f. The doctors stethoscope touched my back.

   _____

   g. Texass oil rigs dominate the landscape.

   _____

   h. The womens race was very exciting.

   _____

I see the sea

Homophones are words which sound the same but have different meanings and spellings: *homo* (same) + *phone* (sound). They are the cause of many mistakes!

- *through* (passing within something from one side to another)
- *threw* (past tense of *throw*)

Sometimes there are three alternative meanings:

- *there* (a place) *their* (belonging to them) *they're* (short for *they are*)

1. **Circle the correct homophone from the words in bold. If in doubt, check in a dictionary.**

   She looked for **they're / their / there** coats.

   We went to **buy / by / bye** sweets.

   It is **too / to / two** hot.

   It went **threw / through** the window.

2. **There are three mistakes in the paragraph below. Find them and rewrite the paragraph correctly on the lines below.**

   Anwar caught the ball and through it to Handa. Unfortunately, it passed bye her into there neighbour's garden, breaking the window.

   _____

   _____

   _____

   _____

A be poem

1. Read this poem below and then rewrite it using the correct homophones.

There was a little be

Who flew across the see

Because he said he new

That the sea was a lovely bright blew

_____

_____

_____

_____

A dear heard

1. **Read the passage below. Circle the incorrect homophones and write the correct versions above.**

I once went walking through a park. It was a beautiful day and I saw a

heard of dear. They sat in the shade of a huge oak tree. The hole heard

was peacefully chewing grass as I walked by. Suddenly, I herd a shout and

a man was chasing towards the deer. He ran so fast that he didn't see a

whole in the ground, he tripped and fell in. Oh deer I thought as he didn't

look very happy climbing back out of the whole.

2. **Now complete the table with the pairs of words you have found.**

Word	Meaning
heard	listened to

Choose the homophone

1. **Choose the correct word to compete these sentences.**

   It is **great** / **grate** that I am going to see my friend.

   I could hear the baby blackbirds **cheep** / **cheap** in their nests.

   After I tripped up, I had a **pain** / **pane** in my leg.

2. **Use a dictionary. In your own words, write the meanings of the homophones from question 1.**

   great

   _____

   grate

   _____

   cheep

   _____

   cheap

   _____

   pain

   _____

   pane

   _____

Homophone sentences

1. **Add the correct homophone to complete the sentences.**

   I had to _____ a letter to my grandparents to thank them for

   my present. **right** / **write**

   You have to wait _____ until the lights turn green. **here** / **hear**

   The match was called off because of the _____.

   whether / **weather**

   You should have _____ the queue for the sale! **seen** / **scene**

2. **Write some sentences to show the meanings of these homophones.**

   knot / not _____

   _____

   _____

   heel / heal / he'll _____

   _____

   _____

   _____

   medal / meddle _____

   _____

   _____

Homophone wordsearch

1. **Write the homophones of these words.**

   fare   _____

   mist   _____

   peace   _____

   grown   _____

2. **Now find all eight words in the wordsearch.**

f	a	r	e	s	s	g	h
a	c	m	r	e	f	h	m
p	o	i	f	a	i	r	i
i	g	s	h	o	d	i	s
e	r	t	i	p	l	a	s
c	o	e	p	e	a	c	e
e	w	s	a	d	r	m	d
x	n	s	g	r	o	a	n

Homophone meanings

1. Match each word to its definition.

rode   The water that falls from the sky.

rein   The length of time a queen stays on the throne.

rain   Horses wear these.

rowed   Cars and lorries use this to get around.

road   You might have done this on a horse.

reign   You might have done this in a boat.

2. Now write a short story using the words from question 1.

_____

_____

_____

_____

_____

_____

_____

_____

Boy overboard

In English, many words which sound the same are spelled differently to show different meanings. Words of this kind are called **homophones**. It is interesting to note dialect differences: *ant* and *aunt* are pronounced in the same way by Northerners but not by Southeners, and *bomb* and *balm* are pronounced the same way by Americans!

1. **Read each sentence, then respell the words in italics so that they give the correct meaning.**

    a. Throw that *boy* _____ overboard!

    b. I enjoy watching *cereals* _____ on television.

    c. There was a long *cue* _____ for snooker yesterday.

    d. I would like a good quality bow made out of *you* _____.

    e. I am sorry to tell you that she *dyed* _____ yesterday.

    f. The baker had to *need* _____ the dough.

    g. Oh, I see that you've had your *hare* _____ done!

    h. This fake *fir* _____ coat is very prickly.

    i. I can't help until I get the *fax* _____.

    j. London has elected a new *mare* _____.

2. **Make up more humorous sentences of the same kind.**

    _____

    _____

Creating nouns (1)

Prefixes are a group of letters that go in front of a word and change the meaning of the word.

- **'hyper'** means *over, beyond, above.*
- **'kilo'** means one *thousand.*
- **'mega'** means *large.*

1. Match each word below with the **'mega'**, **'kilo'** or **'hyper'** prefix to create a new noun. Write the new word in the correct elephant.

market   metre   link   active   byte   gram   star   city

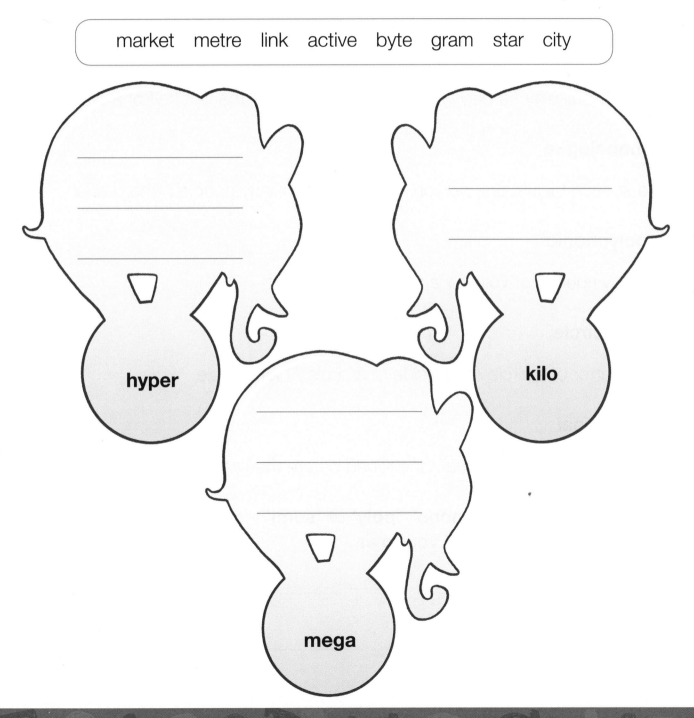

Creating nouns (2)

1. **Find out the meaning of the following prefixes.**

   mono _____

   poly _____

   semi _____

2. **Use your knowledge to circle the correct meaning for these 'mono', 'poly' and 'semi' words.**

   monodrama

   a very dull play / a play with just one performer / the first half of a play

   monologue

   a speech by just one person / a speech for many people / one branch

   polyphonic

   many sounds or voices / a musical instrument

   semicircle

   a quarter of a circle / the inside of a circle / half a circle

   semi-final

   half way through the final / the round before the final / a little final

3. **Choose one of the 'mono', 'poly' or 'semi' words from question 2. Use it in a sentence of your own.**

   _____

   _____

Creating nouns (3)

1. Join the words to the prefixes and then write the noun that is created.

	Prefix	Noun
violet		_____
cover		_____
sound	ultra	_____
port		_____
arm	under	_____
marine		_____
atlantic		_____
ground	trans	_____
late		_____

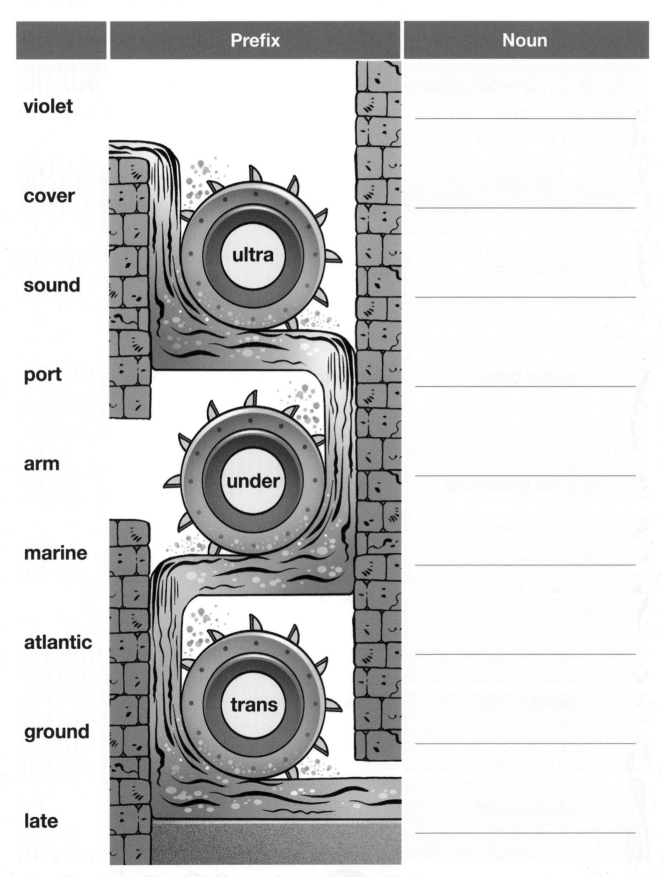

From *aqua* to *aquarium*

Many word families use a **root** from an older language, such as Latin. Knowing the root word and its meaning can help you to increase your vocabulary, and also help you to spell other words from the same family.

1. All of the words below use roots from an older language. Read the root word and then the modern word. Find more modern words that belong to that word family.

Root word	Modern word	More words
aqua (water)	aquarium	
audio (hear)	audience	
centum (hundred)	century	
liber (free)	liberty	
navis (ship)	navy	
plus (more)	surplus	

From *porto* to *porter*

1. Here are some more words with roots from older languages.
   Complete the table by finding more modern words for each word
   family.

Root word	Modern word	More words
porto (carry)	porter	
rota (wheel)	rotate	
scribe (write)	describe	
unus (one)	unit	
vanus (empty)	vanish	
video (see)	video recorder	

Word families (1)

A **word family** is a group of words formed from the same root by adding different **prefixes** and **suffixes**. An example is given below for *electric*.

1. **Make a word family for the word *profess*.**

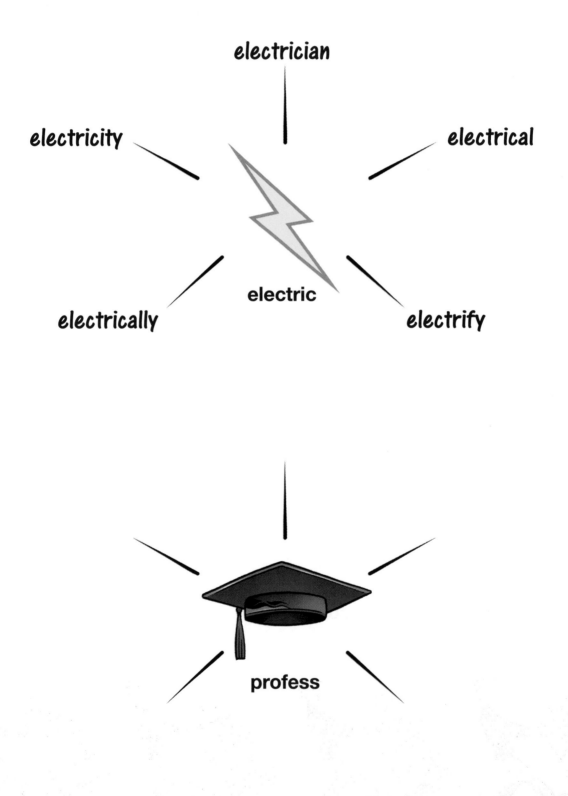

Word families (2)

1. Make word families for these words: *technical* and *sign*.

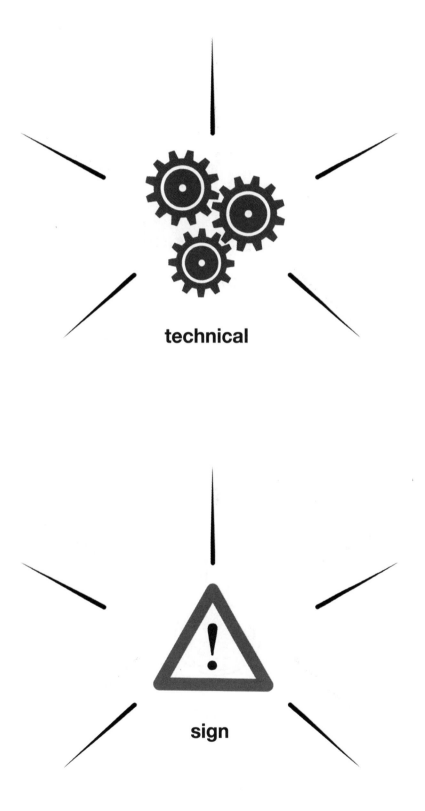

technical

sign

Word families (3)

1. Make word families for these words: *graph* and *science*.

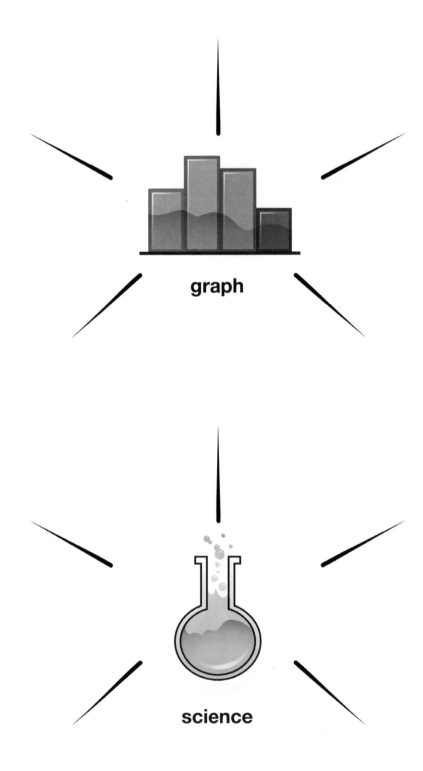

graph

science

Provide a pronoun

1. **Improve the sentences below by replacing a *noun* with a *pronoun* when the noun has been repeated.**

   a. Amra fell heavily. Amra hurt her knee.

   _____

   b. I have a cat. I am very fond of that cat.

   _____

   c. The magnet belongs to Tom. The magnet is very powerful.

   _____

   _____

   d. Debbie and I went to the library to get a book. Debbie and I found the book.

   _____

   _____

   e. James is a tall boy. James is very athletic. I admire James.

   _____

   _____

   f. Jane was very careless. Jane lost her purse. Luckily, on her way home, Jane found her purse.

   _____

   _____

Grammar

Trudy's dream present

Pronouns are used to avoid repetition across sentences.

Read Version 1 of *Trudy's Dream Present*, an example of a writer not using any personal pronouns.

Now read Version 2 of *Trudy's Dream Present*, an example of a writer using too many personal pronouns.

Version 1

Trudy got Trudy's dream present for Christmas – a mobile phone. Trudy couldn't wait to try the mobile phone out, so Trudy dialled a number. Trudy was disappointed when nothing happened. Then Trudy realised that Trudy hadn't turned the mobile phone on. Trudy flicked the switch and tried again, but again Trudy was disappointed because the mobile phone was still dead. Just then, Trudy's friend, Trisha, came into the room. Trudy told Trisha that Trudy had got a mobile phone for Christmas. 'Great, so has Trisha!' said Trisha. 'Trudy and Trisha can call each other!' Trudy said that Trudy had tried but the mobile phone wouldn't work. Trisha asked if Trisha could have a look. Trisha looked at the battery indicator. 'Trisha thought so,' said Trisha. 'Trudy hasn't charged the battery!'

Version 2

She got her dream present for Christmas – a mobile phone. She couldn't wait to try it out, so she dialled a number. She was disappointed when nothing happened. Then she realised that she hadn't turned it on. She flicked the switch and tried again, but again she was disappointed because the phone was still dead. Just then, her friend came into the room. She told her that she had got a mobile phone for Christmas. 'Great, so have I,' she said. 'We can call each other!' She said that she had tried but it wouldn't work. She asked if she could have a look. She looked at the battery indicator. 'I thought so,' said she. 'You haven't charged the battery!'

1. Write your own version of *Trudy's Dream Present* with the right balance of pronouns and proper nouns.

_____

_____

_____

_____

_____

_____

_____

_____

_____

_____

_____

_____

_____

_____

_____

_____

_____

Grammar

Being clear

Using lots of pronouns can make who is doing the actions unclear.

Jack and his friend went to the library. He gave him a book to read.

Who gave who the book? Was it the boy or the friend?

Jack and his friend went to the library. Jack gave his friend a book to read.

It is now clear who gave who the book.

1. **Change some, or all, of the pronouns in these sentences to make them easier to understand.**

   a. Bill went to the park and met John. He gave him a football.

   _____

   _____

   b. In the middle of the field, the girl saw her mum. She beckoned her to come to her.

   _____

   _____

   c. He looked through the window and saw his uncle. He waved at him.

   _____

   _____

   d. He tripped and fell on the ice and pulled over his friend. He helped him up.

   _____

   _____

Expressing time, place and cause (1)

Conjunctions, prepositions and adverbs can express time, place and cause within a sentence and between sentences.

- Time is when something happens: *next, during, immediately.*
- Cause is why something happened: *because.*
- Place is where something happened: *inside.*

1. **Read the passage below and circle any words that express time, place or cause.**

   I went to my friend's house because we were doing our homework together.

   We worked until it was lunchtime. I went back home after I visited the

   library. Since I hadn't finished my homework, I decided to finish it after tea.

   I watched some television then Mum said it was teatime. We had sausage

   and mash and afterwards we had ice cream. The dog was sitting beside the

   table waiting for scraps. My brother went back to watch television while I

   had to finish my homework.

2. **Complete the sentences below with words that express time, place or cause.**

   a. I went to bed _____ I was tired.

   b. We went to the café for lunch _____ we went to the cinema.

   c. I have lived in this house _____ the day I was born.

   d. The boy didn't hand in his homework _____ he got told off.

e. It was left on the floor _____ the rubbish bin.

f. _____ it will be my birthday.

g. I will do my work _____ I will watch some television.

h. I found the key _____ the mess in the drawer

i. I will wait here _____ your train leaves.

j. _____ the performance, the man ate crisps noisily.

3. **Complete the Time Lord's instructions using your choice of time, place and cause words.**

To retrieve my Sonic Abacus please follow these simple

instructions. _____ go quickly downstairs and look

_____ the table for a banana _____ I'm

a bit peckish _____ I've been too busy for breakfast.

_____ we will need the Byzantium Key which your mum is

currently using as a hoover. I left it here _____ my previous

visit and the disguise has worked perfectly! _____ you

have secured the Key I can unlock the Aztec Portal and we'll all be home

_____ elevenses.

Determiners

Sometimes a noun is an item that is well-known to us, for example *my* dog, *that* dog over there.

Sometimes a noun is an item that we don't know well, for example *a* dog, *some* dogs.

All of the words in bold above are called *determiners*. They specify how well we know a noun and can tell us how many, whose and which.

Determiners
the a an three six
many some both first this
that many

Nouns
flower dog boy crocodile
door stairs school children
trees river stars cup

1. **Choose six determiners and six nouns from the chart above. Use them to make up six sentences.**

_____

_____

_____

_____

_____

_____

_____

_____

Expanded noun phrases (1)

Expanded noun phrases give us more information. They can contain adjectives and preposition phrases, as well as the noun.

The girl with the big smile *spoke to her friends.*

1. **Underline the expanded noun phrases in the sentences below.**

   a. I think it was those boys over there!

   b. The big black clouds moved overhead.

   c. I really I like the lesson after maths.

   d. This garden overgrown with weeds was a secret.

   e. The fast red car went speeding down the road.

   f. I saw the silly little kittens in the basket.

   g. You can add the extra words before the noun and after it.

   h. The big black clouds, with a menacing rumble, moved overhead.

2. **Pick two sentences from question 1 and expand the noun phrases further.**

_____

_____

_____

_____

Expanded noun phrases (2)

1. **Underline the simple noun phrases in the sentences below. Then expand them. The first one has been done for you. If there is more than one noun in the sentence you can choose which one to expand.**

   a. I ran under <u>the shelter</u> to get out of the rain.

   I ran under the rusty old bus shelter to get out of the rain.

   b. There are three apples in the bowl.

   _____

   _____

   c. I think it was those boys!

   _____

   _____

   d. I wanted to find a red dress for the party

   _____

   _____

   e. Four horses raced around the track.

   _____

   _____

Describe these pictures

1. Choose four pictures and write a sentence about each of them.
   Include an expanded noun phrase in each sentence.

good witch

bad witch

talking rabbit

fortress of doom

deep dark forest

murky swamp

treasure chest

magic mirror

book of spells

_____

_____

_____

_____

_____

_____

_____

Adverbials

Sometimes, we use more than one word to provide more information about a verb. This is called an **adverbial**.

*The bus leaves **in five minutes**.*

in five minutes tells us when the bus will leave.

An adverbial usually answers questions such as *How?*, *When/How long for?* and *Where?*

1. **Look at the sentences below. Underline the adverbials.**

    a. Jill shut the door quietly.

    b. I promised to meet Bob outside the shop.

    c. The bath, like a bubbly haven, was Sally's ultimate goal of the day.

    d. I will start my homework in a couple of minutes.

    e. I tripped over the bag when I got off the bus.

    f. We met when we started school.

    g. I got to see my favourite band after hours of queuing.

    h. There were chocolates, sweets, biscuits and cakes left by the kind lady.

2. **What do you notice about where the adverbial comes in the sentence?**

    _____

    _____

    _____

    _____

Matching adverbials

Adverbials do not always have to come at the end of a sentence. Sometimes they come at the beginning. When they do, we use a comma after them.

*I'm visiting my grandma **at the weekend**.*

***At the weekend**, I am visiting my grandma.*

1. Add the adverbial to each sentence. First write the adverbial at the end. Then write the sentence again with the adverbial at the beginning – remember the comma!

I will tidy my room.   **Adverbial:** before I do my homework

_____

_____

_____

It will be the holidays.   **Adverbial:** after tomorrow

_____

_____

_____

I tiptoed into the room.   **Adverbial:** slowly and stealthily

_____

_____

_____

Writing fronted adverbials

1. Use these adverbials to write sentences of your own. Only use the adverbials at the beginning of the sentences.

fast and furiously   before we go   when I got off the bus in a flash
after tomorrow   slowly and quietly   impatiently and grumpily
at the end of the week

_____

_____

_____

_____

_____

_____

_____

_____

_____

_____

_____

We was or we were?

Standard English can be spoken or written. It is the form that is usually used in formal writing and it can be used in all accents. It is seen as the 'correct' form.

Non-standard English is usually used in speech and can vary in different places. You would not usually use this for writing.

For example:

- **Standard English: *I did* my homework.**
- **Non-standard English: *I done* my homework.**

1. **Tick each sentence to say whether it is standard English or non-standard English.**

	Non-standard	Standard

I did not see the chair and fell over it.

Yes, I've seen them books.

We was playing at home in my garden.

I ain't felling very well.

I was happy about winning the race.

Me mum says I have to go now.

2. **Choose two of the non-standard sentences from question 1. Rewrite them in standard English.**

_____

_____

I done it well

1. Read the speech bubbles and then change the conversation into standard English.

I done it without her.

You was supposed to help each other.

I were thinking this was faster.

But she don't care about that.

Singular to plural

There are lots of rules about how to show that nouns are plural.

- For most nouns, add **'s'**.
- Nouns ending in **'s'**, **'ss'**, **'sh'**, **'ch'**, **'x'** and **'z'**, add **'es'**.
- Nouns ending in **'y'**, take off the **'y'** and add **'ies'**.
- Nouns ending in **'f'**, take off the **'f'** and add **'ves'**.

1. **Change these sentences from *singular* to *plural* by changing nouns, verbs, pronouns and other words where necessary. An example has been done for you.**

The boy walks his dog.

The boys walk their dogs.

The ship hit the iceberg.

_____

Her tooth hurts badly.

_____

The horse is eating a raw carrot.

_____

The cat chased the mouse through the house.

_____

_____

She heard the echo in the cave.

_____

Plural or possessive?

To make a noun plural you add **'s'**: *jackets*

To show that something or someone belongs to a noun you add an apostrophe then an **'s'**: *Jane's jackets*

If the noun is a plural and already ends in **'s'**, add the apostrophe on the end: *the girls' jackets*

1. **Read these sentences and circle the mistakes. Then rewrite the words correctly.**

There are several birds' in the gardens. _____

The birds nests are in the tree. _____

Ellie Jennings has several pen's in her

pencil case. _____

At St Winifred's, the girls swimming team

and hockey team are fierce rivals. _____

In the shop I saw shoes', trouser, top's and

jumper, but I did not like any of them. _____

Alex kicked the dogs ball over the fence. _____

The girls' are going to find the boys hideout. _____

There are no cakes' in the shop as they

have all been eaten. _____

The apostrophe

Apostrophes can be used to show that a letter is missing:

she is – she's

Apostrophes are also used to show that something belongs to someone or something:

Shane's cup

1. **Correct the sentences below by inserting the apostrophes.**

I didnt want to ask, but I had to find out if they were Joes socks.

There wasnt any food in the cupboard so I took Mums chocolate.

The flowerpot was knocked over by Katies dog.

I hadnt seen the boy run away, but my friends had.

I wasnt going to see my sisters concert.

Somehow I wasnt going to let my brothers prank upset me.

In the end it didnt go according to plan.

Bens football team was winning, but he wasnt there to watch.

The dog's scooter

1. **Match each noun to an object. Write the combinations you have chosen, adding an apostrophe and 's'.**

Jack	lead	_____
a dog	stable	_____
the fish	scooter	_____
the horse	pen	_____
the boy	pond	_____
a girl	bike	_____
the teachers	book	_____
Emily	apple	_____

The cows' garage

Remember: when you add an apostrophe to a plural noun you just add the apostrophe because there is already an **'s'** at the end.

1. **Change the singular nouns into plurals and then match them to an object. Add the apostrophe correctly.**

2. **Complete the final row in the table with your own idea.**

the girl___   school   _____ *the girls' school* _____

the rabbit___   hutch   _____

the boy___   changing room _____

the bird___   nest   _____

the car___   garage   _____

the cow___   field   _____

the _____   _____   _____

Comma time

A comma is used in sentences to separate lists.

1. Rewrite these sentences, adding in the commas in the correct place.

I went swimming and had to bring my costume towel goggles and float.

_____

_____

Leila's dress was an astonishing mix of pink blue red and yellow.

_____

_____

I like eating apples bananas, grapes and pickles.

_____

_____

To get to my friend's house you have to turn left then right and go straight on.

_____

_____

I'd like to play on the slide the climbing frame the swings and the zip wire.

_____

_____

In the field I saw a poppy a cornflower and a butterfly.

_____

At the beginning

An **adverbial** is a group of words that modifies a verb (see page 76). When we use these at the beginning of a sentence, we put a comma after it.

1. **Add the missing comma after the adverbials in these sentences.**

   After school I went to my swimming lessons.

   While I was at the party my mum took my brother to the shops.

   In the morning I will get up and walk the dog.

   After the pantomime we went to have ice cream in the café.

   During the race I tripped up and fell down.

   Later that day he found his book and his pen.

   The day after tomorrow I will be going on holiday.

   Before we start I need to tell you the rules.

Before you go

1. **Complete the sentences by adding the fronted adverbials. Don't forget to add a comma too.**

Before you go

As soon as I'm back

After midnight

In the morning light

Playtime over

In one week's time

_____ I'll be at the concert. Yay!

_____ Hampton Villa was a regular hotel.

_____ it became truly spooky.

_____ don't forget to lock the door.

_____ the class got back to work.

_____ I'll get your dinner ready.

Punctuating direct speech

In direct speech, related punctuation goes inside the speech marks.
One sentence: comma before the tag word inside speech marks.
Speech marks at beginning and end of direct words spoken.

"I can't go out in this weather or I shall get soaked to the skin," said Mo.

Two sentences: comma before tag word inside speech marks.
Full stop after speaker's name. End full stop inside speech marks.
Speech marks close and re-open either side of tag-word and speaker.

"I can't go out in this weather," said Mo. *"I shall get soaked to the skin."*

One sentence, broken in the middle by tag word and speaker's name.
Comma before first close of speech marks, comma after tag word or name,
lower-case letter to continue the sentence after the tag word. Full stop inside
the speech marks at the end.

"I can't go out in this weather," Mo said, *"or I shall get soaked to the skin,
won't I?"*

1. **Punctuate the following sentences.**

   a. In the winter the weather gets cold but snow usually falls
   only on the hills explained Mr Smith

   b. In the summer it is warmer Mr Smith added so the sheep
   will graze on higher ground

   c. In the autumn and spring the weather varies he continued
   Sheep can be found on high and low ground

   d. I am never sure whether I prefer winter or summer said
   Adam but I do like building snowmen

The three little pigs

1. **Add speech marks and commas to the passage to show what the characters said.**

Poor Mrs Porker couldn't find anywhere to lie down. She turned round and round, trying to find a space because she really wanted to take a nap.

First she trod straight on one fat pink piglet.

That's it! cried Mrs Porker. You're far too big to be a piglet she told him. You must go and find your own home.

So First Little Pig left and went off to find a new home. Off I go he sang cheerily, to find a pretty new house.

Mrs Porker tried to find space to lie down again. She turned round and round and trod on the second fat pink piglet.

You're too big to be a piglet she told him. You must go and find your own home.

So Second Little Pig set off to find a new home. Off I go he sang to find a warm new house.

Again Mrs Porker turned round and round and trod on the third fat pink piglet.

You're much too big to be a piglet she told him. Go and find your own home.

So Third Little Pig set off to find a new house. Off I go, he sang cheerily, to find a strong new house.

And so all the Little Pigs trotted off down the road to find new homes.

Mrs Porker turned round and round found a comfy spot and was soon snoring happily.

Presenting dialogue

1. **Read the dialogue between Lucy and her dog Sam. Rewrite it as a passage of text, adding detail about how each speech is spoken. Remember to start a new line for each new speaker and to use the correct punctuation for speech.**

Listen, Sam, that must be the newspaper boy!

Lucy

Woof! Woof!

dog

I wonder if you can remember what you learned at dog school? Take the paper to dad. Now fetch!

Lucy

Oh, Sam.

Lucy's dad

Did it work?

Lucy

Sort of. He fetched the paper but it's all torn.

Lucy's dad

_____

_____

_____

_____

_____

Model dialogue

Look at this example of dialogue and notice the use of punctuation and indentations.

Tim and Tom spent most of the afternoon in the shed trying to make aeroplanes from kits – but everything seemed to go wrong.

"Hey, my aeroplane's got four wings," said Tim.

"Mine hasn't got any," said Tom.

"Mine's got four engines," said Tim.

"Mine must be a glider," said Tom.

Then they realised that they had got the parts of the two kits muddled up and the only thing to do was to pull them to pieces and start again.

1. Use the example to help you write your own short dialogue.

Write a short paragraph to introduce the dialogue.

_____

_____

_____

Now add at least three lines of dialogue.

_____

_____

_____

Write a short paragraph to say what happens next.

_____

_____

_____

Lost wallet

In the passage below, two boys face a dilemma.

The bus slowed down and stopped. It was the stop before school. One man got off, but Balraj and Ben hardly noticed him, until they realised that he had left something behind – a wallet. Balraj picked it up and shouted after the man, but it was too late. The bus had already started again.

He sat back down and Ben said, "Here, let's have a look." Balraj passed over the wallet, and Ben opened it. "Hey, there's a five-pound note here!" he said.

"You're not thinking of keeping it?" said Balraj.

"Why not?" said Ben. "Finders keepers."

"It's not worth being dishonest just for five pounds," said Balraj. "You could earn that quickly just by mowing Granny Smith's lawn!"

"What if it were £1000?" said Ben.

"Er..." Balraj hesitated, "well, I suppose it's still the same! You'd better give that wallet to me and I'll hand it in."

Balraj took the wallet and looked through it. "Look, here's his address," he said after a moment, "and...what's this?"

He took out a folded piece of paper. He unfolded it and spread it out between them. It was a roughly sketched map. The main city on the map was Porto Paso in South America and there was a dotted line to a place marked with compass bearings. Somebody had scribbled near the bearings: 'Inca gold here.'

"It's a treasure map!" exclaimed Ben. "That settles it. We keep the wallet and the map and go and find the treasure. We'll be rich!"

"Find the treasure – what with?" said Balraj. "Do you know how much a ticket to South America will cost?"

"I'll save up for it!"

"Yeah, for about ten years! I think this map makes it even more important to give the wallet back."

Read the passage on page 92 and answer the questions below.

1. What is the dilemma?

_____

2. What do you think the boys should do if this was a real-life incident?

_____

3. What do you think will happen in the story?

_____

4. What stories have you read that have the theme of a dilemma?

_____

5. Here are some dilemmas. Pick one and write two alternate outcomes for it.

> Jenna has promised her mum that she will revise properly for an exam next week. But she has been invited to the cinema tomorrow afternoon.

> Jonathan is ten steps away from the golden statue. But the door to the treasure chamber is closing right NOW.

> Princess Genevieve knows she can outsmart the troll and get back to the castle in time for dinner. But Sir Gifford is trying very hard to impress her.

_____

_____

_____

_____

Heraldry

1. **Read the following passage and underline the key facts.**

When a medieval knight was in full armour his face was covered with a helmet so it was impossible to decide who he was or even for whom he was fighting! In order for his supporters to recognise him, the knight would wear a 'coat of arms' over his armour. This led to the practice of putting the same designs on the shield.

A shield was divided into nine main areas. Across the top of the shield were the 'dexter chief', the 'centre chief' and the 'sinister chief'. Below these were the 'dexter flank', the 'fess point' (the centre of the shield) and the 'sinister flank'. The bottom third of the shield was divided into 'dexter base', the 'centre base' and the 'sinister base'.

In Latin, 'dexter' means right and 'sinister' means left, but a shield was always decorated as seen from the point of view of the knight *behind* the shield.

Only certain colours were used to paint the shield – red, blue, black, green and purple – and only two metals could be used – silver and gold. The knights also chose to divide the shield with horizontal, vertical or chevron lines. Finally they added drawings of things such as griffins, eagles, rampant lions, trees, flowers and weapons. When one rich family married another their shield emblems were often combined and became more complicated.

Glossary

chevron a V shape

griffin an animal that is part eagle, part lion

rampant standing on its back legs

coat of arms a decorated tunic

---

2. Use the key facts you found to summarise the text in one paragraph.

_____

_____

_____

_____

_____

_____

_____

3. Now decorate the shield following the instructions below and using the information given in the passage.

- three horizontal lines in dexter chief
- a sun in fess point
- three vertical lines in sinister chief
- five horizontal lines which cover dexter base and centre base
- two chevrons in the dexter flank
- a rampant lion which covers sinister flank and sinister base
- a bird in the centre chief
- Colour your shield in suitable colours.

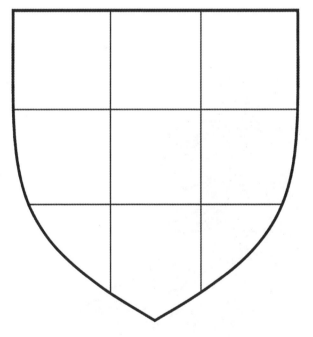

! Don't forget left is right as you look at the shield.

Cats

Cats sleep

Anywhere,

Any table,

Any chair,

Top of piano,

Window-ledge,

In the middle,

On the edge,

Open drawer,

Empty shoe,

Anybody's

Lap will do,

Fitted in a

Cardboard box,

In the cupboard

With your frocks –

Anywhere!

They don't care!

Cats sleep

Anywhere.

Eleanor Farjeon

The dog's scooter

1. **Match each noun to an object. Write the combinations you have chosen, adding an apostrophe and 's'.**

Jack	lead	_____
a dog	stable	_____
the fish	scooter	_____
the horse	pen	_____
the boy	pond	_____
a girl	bike	_____
the teachers	book	_____
Emily	apple	_____

The cows' garage

Remember: when you add an apostrophe to a plural noun you just add the apostrophe because there is already an **'s'** at the end.

1. Change the singular nouns into plurals and then match them to an object. Add the apostrophe correctly.

2. Complete the final row in the table with your own idea.

the girl___	school	_the girls' school_
the rabbit___	hutch	
the boy___	changing room	
the bird___	nest	
the car___	garage	
the cow___	field	
the _____	_____	

Poets often use **rhyming words** at the end of poem lines. This helps to give a poem interesting sound effects.

Read the poem on page 96 and answer the questions.

1. Write pairs of rhyming words from the poem 'Cats'.

   anywhere   _chair_ _____   _____

   _____   _____

Adjectives give extra details about nouns. They help to make the language of poetry rich and atmospheric.

2. Write down three adjectives from the poem 'Cats'.

   _____   _____

   _____

3. What words are repeated in 'Cats'?

   _____

   What effect does this repetition give?

   _____

4. Draw a box around your favourite section of the poem. Explain why you like it.

   _____

   _____

Definitions

Some non-fiction books contain **glossaries** – a lists of words, mostly topic-related, with their definitions. Glossaries are different from dictionaries.

1. Compare words in the glossary of *Heraldry* on page 94 to the same words in a dictionary. Then fill in the chart below. Write a tick ✔ or a cross ✗.

rampant   chevron   coat of arms   griffin

	Dictionary	Glossary
Does the entry give the word meaning?		
Does the entry tell you the type of word it is, e.g. noun?		
Does the entry give you the plural form?		
Does the entry tell you the word origin?		
Does the entry tell you how to pronounce the word?		

2. **Does a dictionary give more information about a word than a glossary?**   Yes ☐ No ☐

3. **Why doesn't a glossary need to tell you what type of word it is?**

_____

4. **Is it important to know how to pronounce a word? Why?**

_____

Easy tent

1. Read the EASY-TENT instructions.

a. Circle the following and label them: list of what is needed, sequenced steps.

b. Find any command verbs and highlight them.

c. Find any words expressing time and highlight them in a different colour.

How to set up your EASY-TENT

1. Check that you have everything you need:
   - The green outer tent
   - Fully charged batteries
   - The white inner tent
   - 8 large plastic pegs
   - The super pump

2. Connect the super pump to the inlet valve on the green outer tent by removing the red cap, and screwing the plastic hose into position.

3. Switch on the super pump. After about five minutes, the green outer tent should have risen to a dome shape. When this is firm and round, switch off the pump and remove the plastic hose. A one-way valve will stop the air escaping, but remember to replace the red cap just to make sure! Note: if the pump fails or the batteries go flat, you will find an emergency nozzle near the inlet valve. Use this to blow up the tent by mouth.

4. Important: Immediately peg the green tent to the ground by placing pegs through all of the eight loops. The EASY-TENT is very light and may get blown away if you forget to do this!

5. Place the white inner tent inside the green outer tent and pump up in the same way.

6. Your EASY-TENT is now ready. Enjoy your holiday!

Story order

The plot of a story is the sequence of main events. This is what happens to your characters at the beginning, middle and then the end.

Introduction: The characters are introduced, the setting described and the theme established.

Build up: What is happening to the characters – often more about the theme.

Conflict: The actions of solving the problem/mystery.

Climax: When the characters are about to solve the problem/mystery and it looks like it either could be solved or not.

Resolution: The problem/mystery is solved and how the characters are affected by the outcome.

They had not gone far when their jeep was stopped by a tree which had fallen across the trail. As soon as they got out to move it, they found themselves surrounded by bandits with AK47 rifles. Tom groaned, and Lindsey wept – but Paco laughed. He knew these men, and after a few words in Spanish, and the gift of a bottle of whisky, they were on their way again.

Tom had heard the legend of the 'Dinosaurs on Dinosaur Plateau' and decided that he would like to be the first to bring back a real dinosaur egg. So he gave up his job as a Geography teacher and set out with his wife, Lindsey, for Porto Paso.

After a difficult climb, they reached the Plateau. There was a movement in bushes ahead, and a creature lifted its head to look at them. The head was huge, scaly and had rows of sharp teeth.
    "A dinosaur!" shouted Tom.
    "No," said Lindsey sadly, "only a monitor lizard".

When they arrived in Porto Paso, they bought a jeep and supplies for a month. Hiring a local guide was more difficult. They seemed afraid of bandits, gorillas and hostile tribes – but most of all, of the dinosaurs that they thought were living on the plateau. At last they found an old man who agreed to be their guide. His name was Paco.

Read the story sections on page 100.

1. Number the story section paragraphs in the correct order. Write 1–4 in the boxes.

2. Write what you think is the main point of each paragraph.

    1. _____

    2. _____

    3. _____

    4. _____

3. The resolution of this story is missing. Write your own ending below.

    _____

    _____

    _____

    _____

    _____

    _____

Water cycle

The Earth's water is 97 per cent salt water and 3 per cent fresh water. Of the fresh water, 17 per cent is free-flowing and 83 per cent is frozen. So only a tiny part of Earth's water is for people, plants and animals to share. Since the amount of water is constant, we must use the fresh water over and over again.

Different states

Water is the only substance to exist naturally as three states of matter. Water is found as a solid when it freezes to form ice. It freezes at 0 °C. Above 0 °C, it melts to form liquid water. When liquid water is heated, it evaporates and turns into a gas called water vapour. Water can evaporate at almost any temperature above freezing. For example, the water in wet washing will evaporate even on a cool day.

How clouds form

Water evaporates from the surface of rivers, lakes, seas and oceans, and from the leaves of plants. As water vapour rises, it cools. It condenses back to form tiny droplets of water. Millions of these droplets form rain clouds. With more moisture, the droplets get bigger and then fall to the ground.

An endless cycle

Water droplets that fall from clouds are called precipitation. Some precipitation is soaked up by the ground and plants. Some drains into rivers, lakes, seas and oceans, where it evaporates and the whole process begins again. This is called the water cycle.

Read the text on page 102 and then answer the questions below.

1. **What kind of text is this?**

   Instruction ☐

   Report ☐

   Explanation ☐

2. **What are the features of this text, for example headings, subheadings?**

   _____

   _____

3. **Find and write any words expressing cause.**

   _____

   _____

4. **Summarise the text in five sentences.**

   _____

   _____

   _____

   _____

   _____

Haiku

Haiku (pronouned *high-coo*) is a Japanese form of poetry. It is unrhymed, and short! It only has 17 syllables, arranged in three lines of 5 syllables, 7 syllables and 5 syllables.

Remember: each beat in a word is a syllable, so *stair* has one syllable, *footsteps* has two syllables, and so on.

1. **Read these haiku poems aloud. Clap and count the syllables in each line.**

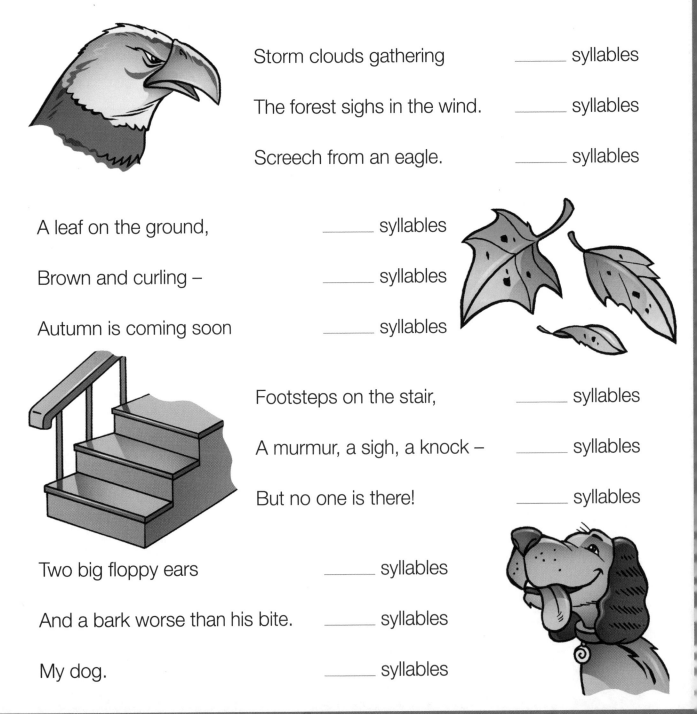

Storm clouds gathering _____ syllables

The forest sighs in the wind. _____ syllables

Screech from an eagle. _____ syllables

A leaf on the ground, _____ syllables

Brown and curling – _____ syllables

Autumn is coming soon _____ syllables

Footsteps on the stair, _____ syllables

A murmur, a sigh, a knock – _____ syllables

But no one is there! _____ syllables

Two big floppy ears _____ syllables

And a bark worse than his bite. _____ syllables

My dog. _____ syllables

2. Look back at your answers to question 1. Rewrite the two incorrect haiku so they complete the rule about syllables.

The Railway Children

Characters are very important to a story. However, not everything about a character is described. The reader must also make **inferences** to understand the characters better.

From Chapter 1 *(in their old home)*

There were three of them. Roberta was the eldest. Of course, Mothers never have favourites, but if their Mother had had a favourite, it might have been Roberta. Next came Peter, who wished to be an Engineer when he grew up; and the youngest was Phyllis, who meant extremely well.

Mother did not spend all her time in paying dull calls to dull ladies, and sitting dully at home waiting for dull ladies to pay calls to her. She was almost always there, ready to play with the children, and read to them, and help them do their home-lessons. Besides this she used to write stories while they were at school, and read them aloud after tea, and she always made up funny pieces of poetry for their birthdays and for other great occasions, such as the christening of the new kittens, or the refurnishing of the doll's house, or the time when they were getting over the mumps.

From Chapter 11 *(inside a railway tunnel)*

The roar of the advancing train was now louder than the noise you hear when your head is under water in the bath and both taps are running, and you are kicking with your heels against the bath's tin sides. But Peter had shouted for all he was worth, and Bobbie heard him. She dragged Phyllis along to the manhole. Phyllis, of course, tumbled over the wires and grazed both her legs. But they dragged her in, and all three stood in the dark, damp, arch recess while the train roared louder and louder. It seemed as if it would deafen them. And, in the distance, they could see its eyes of fire growing bigger and brighter every instant.

"It is a dragon – I always knew it was – it takes its own shape in here, in the dark," shouted Phyllis. But nobody heard her. You see the train was shouting, too, and its voice was bigger than hers.

E Nesbit

1. **Read the two extracts on page 106 and then complete the chart below.**

Character	Facts	Inferences (and supporting text reference)
Roberta	The eldest child Called Bobbie for short Has had the mumps	Close to her mother. ("if Mother had a favourite… might have been Roberta") Quick thinking, responsible and practical. ("She dragged Phyllis along to the manhole.")
Peter		
Phyllis		
Mother		
The family as a whole		

Two eagle poems

The Eagle

He clasps the crag with crooked hands;
Close to the sun in lonely lands,
Ringed with the azure world, he stands.

The wrinkled sea beneath him crawls;
He watches from his mountain walls,
And like a thunderbolt he falls.

Alfred Lord Tennyson (1809–1892)

eagle

eagle
majestic appearance
power of flight,
king of birds

since ancient times symbol
of strength and courage
Sumerians 5000 years ago
Imperial Rome
America

but a killer
a dive bomber
with laser sights
that always hits its target

Malcolm George (1950–)

Read the poems and then answer the questions.

1. What are these poems about? _____

2. Which of the poems rhymes? How does it rhyme?

   _____

3. What type of poem is 'eagle'?

   rhyming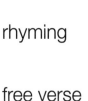

   free verse

   haiku

   Free verse a poem that doesn't follow any rules about rhyming or how to write it.

   Haiku a poem that follows strict rules of using only three lines and only using words which make up five syllables on the first and last lines and seven on the middle line.

4. Why does the poet of 'The Eagle' use the word *thunderbolt* when describing the eagle?

   _____

5. Why does the poet in the second poem write it as a list?

   _____

6. What does *laser sights* mean in the last verse?

   _____

7. Which poem do you prefer, and why?

   _____

   _____

Skyliner journey

Dear Sir

I have just got back from my holiday in New York by Skyliner and I have several complaints.

My first complaint is that Skyliner was SLOW! It took 11 hours to get from London to New York, though your advertisement promised eight hours. What is the point of a new type of air transport if it is slower than the types we already have?

Another point is that I did not get a private cabin. I had to sit in an aeroplane-type seat (though I admit there was plenty of space for my legs). Also, I was not allowed in the glass-bottomed swimming pool. This was very disappointing, because I had looked forward to 'swimming through the sky' as you promised in your advertisement.

It was good to be able to sit at a table for a meal, although you did not say in your advertisement that the cost of the meal was extra. Furthermore, the prices were shocking! I had to pay £25 for pizza, sausage and beans!

I was also very disappointed that the observation deck was open only for the last hour of the journey – and then it got very crowded. However, I must say how much I enjoyed flying over New York and ending our journey at the mooring pole on top of the Statue of Liberty.

Overall, I think Skyliner has some good points, but you need to sort out the problems I have mentioned, and make your advertising more honest. Also, I hope you will be able to offer some compensation for the disappointments suffered.

Yours faithfully

Joe Bloggs

Read the letter and then answer the questions below.

1. **What is Skyliner?**

   A new type of water transport ☐

   A new type of air transport ☐

   A new type of land transport ☐

2. **List three complaints from the letter.**

   _____

   _____

3. **Find and write any words that provoke emotion and any which have been repeated.**

   _____

4. **Can you find the following sentence types in the passage? Write examples.**

   Statements ☐ _____

   Exclamations ☐ _____

   Questions ☐ _____

5. **What is the writer trying to persuade Skyliner Ltd to do?**

   _____

   _____

Paragraphs

Paragraphs help to structure your writing, making it easier to read. Paragraphs are used to group information and are organised around a theme.

1. **Read the following text and then write what you think is the main theme of each paragraph.**

In South America there is a tall mountain range called the Andes. The air is thin and cold there and so people have to keep warm by wearing thick woollen capes called ponchos.

Introduces the story and the setting, for example what it is like in the mountains.

On one of the mountains is a farm. It belongs to the family of a small boy called Pedro. Pedro's family don't live at the farm. They have a house in the city but visit their farm once a year.

_____

_____

One cold day Pedro's father took him to visit their farm. They rode on horseback up the mountain.

_____

The farm dogs started barking. One dog was small and friendly. When Pedro called to it, the dog wagged its tail. When he jumped down from his horse the dog licked Pedro's hand, "It looks like you've made a friend!" laughed Pedro's father.

_____

_____

_____

Later that day, Pedro's father decided they should set off home. They mounted their horses and set off down the mountain. The dog, quietly followed his new friend all the way home!

_____

_____

Writing paragraphs

1. Read the text below and organise the story into sections about a theme. Decide when the story starts, when the time changes and when the place changes. Mark these changes with the symbol //.

It was the morning of the big game. James snuggled into the warmth of his duvet, thinking nervously about the day ahead of him. At 8 o'clock his alarm rang. He sighed. This meant he had to get up. He flung back the duvet and eased his feet into his slippers. Finally he made his way across the room. In the kitchen his dad was cooking breakfast. James knew his dad was only trying to help, but he felt too sick to eat. Across the street Ezzie was ready. As he put new laces in his boots he thought about winning the match. He was sure his team would win. He couldn't wait.

2. Write the next two paragraphs in the story.

Flying machines

In non-fiction writing, paragraphs are sometimes introduced by **subheadings**.

1. **Read the passage about flying machines and pick out four separate paragraphs grouping related material. Mark the beginning of each paragraph with the symbol //.**

For centuries man has dreamed of being able to fly. As long ago as the 15th century, Leonardo da Vinci drew sketches of flying machines. However, he was ahead of his time and his machines were impossible to build with the tools of the day. Man's first successful flight took place in 1783. The Montgolfier brothers filled a large paper balloon with hot smoke from a fire, and it floated 1800 metres into the air. To the people watching, it seemed a miracle, but balloons and airships soon became common. The first flight by an aeroplane took place in 1903, at Kitty Hawk, in the USA. The aeroplane had been made by two brothers, Orville and Wilbur Wright. Though gliders had been flown successfully for many years, the importance of this invention was that it allowed for long-distance flight. The most exciting flight of all must be the journey to the moon. On 20 July,1969, United States astronauts Neil Armstrong and Edwin Aldrin took off in one of the mighty Apollo rockets and travelled to the moon. They landed in the Sea of Tranquillity. They did several experiments, and then took off for Earth with soil and rock samples. After a trouble-free flight, they landed safely.

2. **Think of a suitable subheading for each paragraph you identified. Write them below.**

1. _____   3. _____

2. _____   4. _____

Life cycle of a flowering plant

Use the illustrations to write paragraphs on the life cycle of a plant. Each picture will help to group information about each step in the life cycle.

Characters in adventure stories

When you plan a story it is important to plan your **characters**. The characters are who your story is about. Your characters will also help you plan your setting and your plot.

1. List words which describe the behaviours and personalities of adventure story heroes/heroines and villains.

Heroes and heroines

Ideas

helpful   selfish   unkind   determined   inconsiderate
devious   cowardly   thoughtful   trustworthy   hurts others
helps others   never gives up

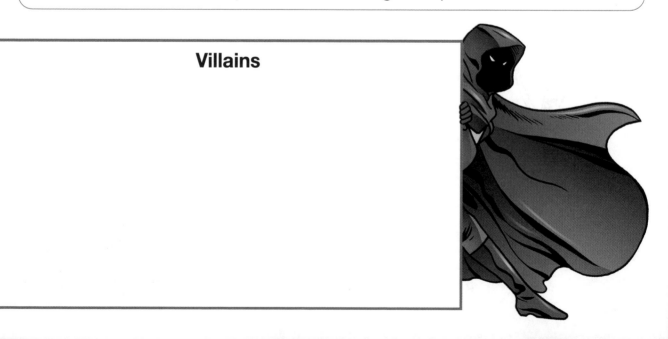

Villains

Into the picture

1. What are these people thinking? What are they saying? Where have they come from? Where are they going? Write some of your ideas in the boxes.

Alien planet and other settings

Planning the **settings** of your story is important.

When you plan your settings ask yourself the question: What can your character see, smell or hear? This will start to create the picture of the settings. Think about the weather. A story set in the mountains might have snowy weather, whereas a story set at the beach might have sunny weather.

Alien planet

Theme park

Factory

1. **Choose one of the pictures above as a setting for a story. Look at the scene carefully, then develop it in note form by:**

 • thinking of adjectives and figures of speech to describe it

 • drawing a map of the area and adding place names and other details, especially those which could be used in a story, such as a deep well.

Develop the setting

1. Continue the setting description.

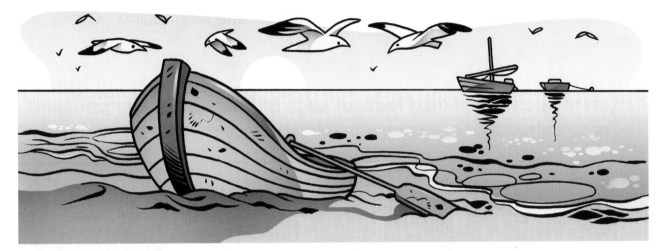

The sand felt hot and grainy under his bare feet. The tide was out and a wide stretch of shining brown mud lay between him and the water.

_____

_____

_____

_____

_____

_____

_____

_____

_____

Hints: What else can he feel? What can he hear? What else can he see?

Planet in danger story

The **plot** describes the main events in the story, the problems your character faces and how they are resolved through the introduction, build up, conflict, climax and resolution.

1. **List the possible side effects of each of these planetary problems. Try to suggest one way in which each problem could be solved.**

Food starts to run out

Effects _____

Solution _____

A strange disease breaks out

Effects _____

Solution _____

Poisonous fumes start to poison the air

Effects _____

Solution _____

Attack by another planet

Effects _____

Solution _____

2. Use the story mountain to plan a story about a problem faced by beings on a planet. Remember to include progression in your plot for the story's beginning, middle and end.

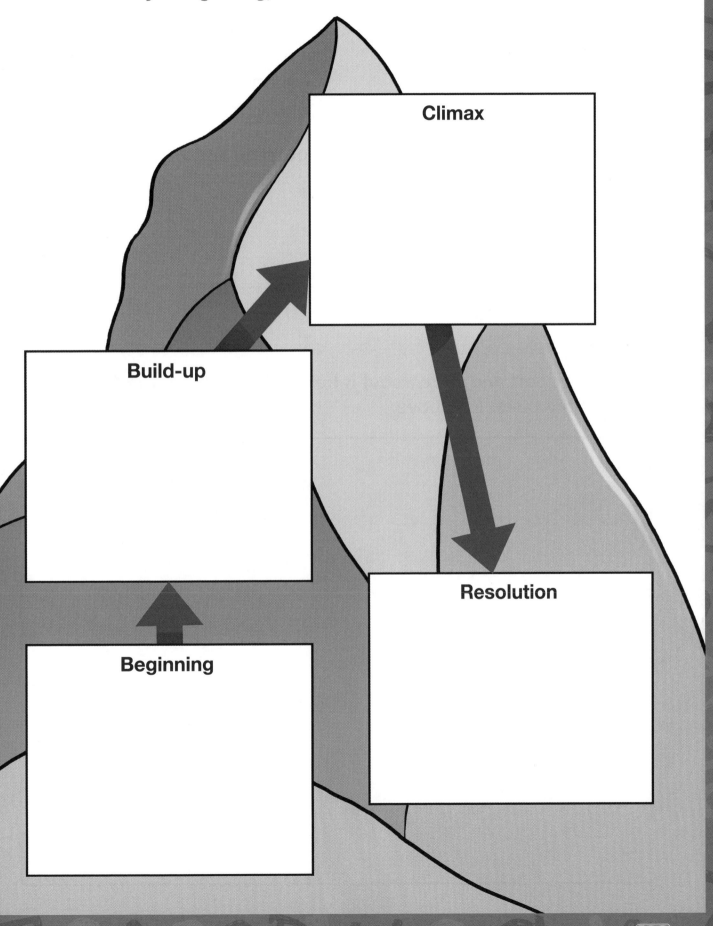

Climax

Build-up

Resolution

Beginning

Taking exercise

Explanations often use:

- clear steps to explain how something happens and why
- illustrations/photos/diagrams with labels/captions
- subheadings
- words to express time and cause
- specific detail

1. Exercise is good for our bodies. Find out why and write down three reasons.

   1. _____

   2. _____

   3. _____

2. Choose a sport and write about it here using some of the features given in the bullet list above.

Driving guide

Instructions must always follow a clear and correct order.

1. **Number the instructions for 'Setting off' in the correct order.**

    Setting off

    ☐ As the car gains speed, change gear until you are in top gear.

    ☐ Check that the car is in neutral gear.

    ☐ Check that the handbrake is on.

    ☐ If all is clear, release the handbrake, and pull out.

    ☐ Check in the mirror.

    ☐ Engage first gear.

    ☐ Get in the car.

    ☐ Put your seatbelt on.

    ☐ Start the engine.

2. **Write instructions for a driver approaching traffic lights. Don't forget instructions have:**
    - a clear sequence of numbered steps
    - command-style verbs at the beginning of each step
    - specific detail (measurements)
    - words expressing time (*next, then*).

_____

_____

_____

_____

Five-point plan

1. **Choose one of the questions in the box below. Use the planning frame to write the first draft of a piece of writing in which you present your point of view on the topic.**

> Should children wear school uniform?   Should chocolate be banned?
> Should children go to school?

Make a point: state your main point and give reasons to support it.

Add another point: give reasons to support it.

Introduce an opposing point: state the opposition's strongest point and give reasons against it.

Discuss the ideas: compare what would happen with your ideas and those of the opposition.

Sum up: state the conclusion you have come to and why.

African elephants

1. **Use the fact card to write a report about elephants. Choose an appropriate heading and then use the words in bold as subheadings.**

Remember to include:
- an introductory sentence
- technical/specific vocabulary
- factual descriptions.

African elephant

Appearance large four-legged animals, grey in colour, long trunk), tusks, large rounded ears

Habitat savannah landscape in Africa, elephants live in herds

Food leaves, branches, grasses, bark, fruit

Average life span 70 years

Size height 2.5m to 4m

Fiction writing frame

1. Use this planning sheet to help you plan a story.

Character	Setting
What do they look like? What is their personality like? Do they have a family? Where do they live? What are they doing?	Where do they live? What does it look like – in the mountains, by the beach, in a city?

Plot

Introduction

Build up

Conflict

Climax

Resolution

Remember to use:
- capital letters
- end of sentence punctuation
- speech marks (if you have dialogue)
- conjunctions, prepositions and adverbs.

Tip: Try to group your ideas about what happens to your character as this will help you to write paragraphs.

2. Now write your story on a separate sheet of paper.

Non-fiction writing frame

1. How do we travel on the water? What do we travel on? Make a list in the lighthouse on the right.

2. Choose one form of water travel and find out as much as you can about it. When was it invented? How does it move? What is it made from? What else can you find out?

_____

_____

_____

_____

_____

_____

_____

_____

_____

_____

_____

3. Now write about your choice on a separate sheet of paper.

Progress chart

Making progress? Tick (✔) the flower boxes as you complete each section of the book.

Spelling

Vocabulary

Punctuation

Composition

Grammar

✂ -

Well done!

YOU DID IT! ★

Name: _____

You have completed
YEAR 4 ENGLISH
Practice Book

Age: _____   Date: _____